外婆的纽扣宝盒

【美】琳达·威廉姆斯·亚伯◎著
【美】佩奇·伊斯特伯恩·欧鲁克◎绘
范晓星◎译

天津出版传媒集团

新蕾出版社

U0266018

图书在版编目（CIP）数据

外婆的纽扣宝盒/(美)亚伯(Aber,L.W.)著；(美)欧鲁克(O'Rourke,P.E.)绘；范晓星译.
—天津：新蕾出版社,2014.1(2024.12重印)
(数学帮帮忙·互动版)
书名原文:Grandma's Button Box
ISBN 978-7-5307-5895-3

Ⅰ.①外…
Ⅱ.①亚…②欧…③范…
Ⅲ.①数学–儿童读物
Ⅳ.①O1–49

中国版本图书馆 CIP 数据核字(2013)第 270452 号

出版发行: 天津出版传媒集团
新蕾出版社

http://www.newbuds.com.cn

地 址:	天津市和平区西康路 35 号(300051)
出 版 人:	马玉秀
电 话:	总编办 (022)23332422
	发行部 (022)23332679　23332351
传 真:	(022)23332422
经 销:	全国新华书店
印 刷:	天津新华印务有限公司
开 本:	787mm×1092mm　1/16
印 张:	3
版 次:	2014 年 1 月第 1 版　2024 年 12 月第 24 次印刷
定 价:	12.00 元

无处不在的数学

资深编辑　卢　江

　　人们常说"兴趣是最好的老师",有了兴趣,学习就会变得轻松愉快。数学对于孩子来说或许有些难,因为比起语文,数学显得枯燥、抽象,不容易理解,孩子往往不那么喜欢。可许多家长都知道,学数学对于孩子的成长和今后的生活有多么重要。不仅数学知识很有用,学习数学过程中获得的数学思想和方法更会影响孩子的一生,因为数学素养是构成人基本素质的一个重要因素。但是,怎样才能让孩子对数学产生兴趣呢?怎样才能激发他们兴致勃勃地去探索数学问题呢?我认为,让孩子读些有趣的书或许是不错的选择。读了这套"数学帮帮忙",我立刻产生了想把它们推荐给教师和家长朋友们的愿望,因为这真是一套会让孩子爱上数学的好书!

　　这套有趣的图书从美国引进,原出版者是美国资深教育专家。每本书讲述一个孩子们生活中的故事,由故事中出现的问题自然地引入一个数学知识,然后通过运用数学知识解决问题。比如,从帮助外婆整理散落的纽扣引出分类,从为小狗记录藏骨头的地点引出空间方位等等。故事素材全部来源于孩子们的真实生活，不是童话，不是幻想，而是鲜活的生活实例。正是这些发生在孩子身边的故事，让孩子们懂得，数学无处不在并且非常有用；这些鲜活的实例也使得抽象的概念更易于理解，更容易激发孩子学习数学的兴趣，让他们逐渐爱上数学。这样的教育思想和方法与我国近年来提倡的数学教育理念是十分吻合的！

这是一套适合5~8岁孩子阅读的书，书中的有趣情节和生动的插画可以将抽象的数学问题直观化、形象化，为孩子的思维活动提供具体形象的支持。如果亲子共读的话，家长可以带领孩子推测情节的发展，探讨解决难题的办法，让孩子在愉悦的氛围中学到知识和方法。

值得教师和家长朋友们注意的是，在每本书的后面，出版者还加入了"互动课堂"及"互动练习"，一方面通过一些精心设计的活动让孩子巩固新学到的数学知识，进一步体会知识的含义和实际应用；另一方面帮助家长指导孩子阅读，体会故事中数学之外的道理，逐步提升孩子的阅读理解能力。

我相信孩子读过这套书后一定会明白，原来，数学不是烦恼，不是包袱，数学真能帮大忙！

凯莉和表姐弟们到外婆家过暑假。一天早上，凯莉起床后，发现家里静悄悄的。三个表姐弟都还在睡觉。外婆出门散步去了。

凯莉独自吃过早餐，琢磨着该玩什么好。

孩子们：
我去散步了，9:00回来。
外婆

蒂米画

凯莉画

盐 胡椒

5

　　凯莉心想:玩什么才不会把他们吵醒呢?看电
视太吵了,弹钢琴太响了,投篮声音也很大。

正在凯莉换衣服时，她听到很小的一声"啪"！
原来是衣服上掉了一枚扣子。

"就玩这个了！"她说，"外婆的纽扣宝盒！"

外婆有很多特别有趣的宝贝纽扣！即使样式很普通，也似乎都非同寻常，因为外婆总能讲出纽扣背后的故事。

盒子里有外婆婚纱上面的珍珠纽扣，有凯莉还是小宝宝时毛衣上面的小火车纽扣，还有软软的毛绒纽扣和一枚看起来很高级的金色纽扣，上面还镶嵌着大宝石呢。

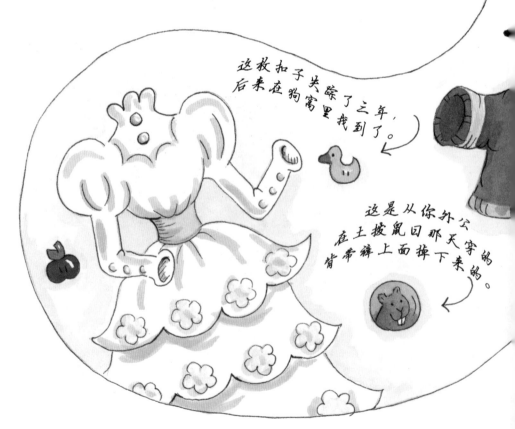

这枚扣子失踪了三年，后来在狗窝里找到了。

这是从你外公在土拨鼠日那天穿的背带裤上面掉下来的。

布兰登演奏大号
的时候，这枚扣子
从衣服上掉了下来。

这枚扣子被
小沙鼠啃掉一牙。

这是罗伊
小时候衣服上的。

这枚扣子是
在鱼缸里发现的。

凯莉整个夏天还没有拿出这个纽扣宝盒玩
呢。玩这个一定不会出什么声响的，她心想。

纽扣宝盒放在外婆缝纫桌旁边的高架子上。凯莉不得不爬上板凳使劲去够。

她尽全力伸长胳膊。

外婆的纽扣宝盒一歪，盒盖"啪嗒"一下开了，扣子也满天飞。稀里哗啦！盒子重重地掉到了地板上。

蒂米和布兰登跑进客厅。

"出了什么事？"布兰登问。然后，他看见了满地的扣子。"天哪！"他说。

"你闯祸了！"蒂米说。

"你们一定要帮我呀!"凯莉说,"我一个人永远也捡不完这么多扣子啊!"

"没问题!"布兰登回答。

"要是你请我去打保龄球的话,我就帮你。"蒂米说。

"一言为定!"凯莉回答。

于是,三个人趴在地上到处找扣子。

"看！花盆里有一枚。"布兰登说。

"外婆的拖鞋里也有一枚。"蒂米大叫。

12

凯莉爬进储物间。"这里有好几枚！"她喊道。

"啊！"蒂米说，"我在地毯下面又找到了六枚！"

很快，扣子堆成了一大堆。

"好乱啊！"蒂米说，"我把它们放回盒子里吧。"

"等一下！"凯莉说，"我们得把扣子按照原来的位置放回小格子里。"

　　"可外婆原来是怎么放的呢？"布兰登问，"按大
小分类的？还是按形状？按颜色？"

　　"我不记得了。"凯莉回答。

　　"天哪！"布兰登说。

　　"你可闯大祸了！"蒂米说。

"也许它们是按照形状分类的。"凯莉说。

"那咱们试试看吧。"布兰登说。

蒂米把所有的圆形扣子都挑了出来。

布兰登挑出了一些方形纽扣，还挑出一些形状像三角形和菱形的扣子。

凯莉开始挑出其他形状的扣子。她找到了星星形状的、鸭子形状的、小船形状的和牛仔靴形状的。还有一枚雨伞形状的、两枚苹果形状的、一枚大象形状的和一枚菠萝形状的扣子。

　　"到底该怎么分类呢？"凯莉问。

　　"这可难住我了！"布兰登说。

　　"按大小分类怎么样？"凯莉说。

　　"你是说我们还得再分一次呀？"蒂米问。

过了一会儿，他们分出了七堆纽扣。

"咱们看看吧！"凯莉说，"我们有超
级小的、小的、中不溜儿的、大的、特别大
的，还有巨大的和超级大的。"

　　凯莉叹了一口气说："这样分也不对。"

　　"这个盒子里有十二个小格子。"布兰登说，"可是我们只分出了七种大小的纽扣。"

　　"我不干了！"蒂米大喊。

"你们在喊什么呢？"年纪最大的表姐莎拉问道。

"凯莉把外婆的纽扣宝盒碰翻了，现在这些扣子全都乱套了。"蒂米说。

"我们试着按照形状分类。"凯莉说。

"可是不对！"蒂米说。

"我们还尝试根据大小分类。"布兰登说。

"可是也不对！"蒂米说。

　　莎拉看看地上的那些扣子。"一定还有其
他方法。"她说,"如果……"

　　"按照颜色分类!"凯莉说。

　　"没错!"莎拉说。

莎拉和凯莉挑出了白色、粉色、紫色、黄色、橙色和棕色的扣子。

布兰登和蒂米则挑出了红色、蓝色、绿色、银色、金色和黑色的扣子。

"正好十二种颜色！"凯莉说。

"每个小格子里面放一种颜色的扣子！"
布兰登说，"大功告成啦！"

"终于分好了！"蒂米说。

"喂，孩子们！"过了一会儿，外婆喊道，
"我回家了！"

"我们在您的缝纫间里！"莎拉喊道。

"天哪！"外婆说，"你们把我的纽扣分类了！"

"凯莉把盒子打翻了。"蒂米说，"可是我们又把纽扣全都找到了。"

"我们按照颜色分类后放回到了纽扣盒。"凯莉说，"您原来就是这样放的，对不对？"

"没有啊！"外婆说，"我不是这样放的。"
"你的麻烦可超级大了！"蒂米对凯莉说。

外婆笑了。"我从来就没有给纽扣分过类啊，宝贝们。"她对凯莉说，"它们就是混在一起放的。"

"那我们全白忙了？"蒂米说。

　　"不会白忙的。"外婆说着,脱下毛衣,"看这儿有两
个别针吧?我一直懒得找新扣子缝上去,因为每次在那
个纽扣盒里找扣子总会花很长时间。"

　　"那我们现在就来找些合适的新扣子吧。"凯莉说,
"根本不会花那么长时间了。"

"这枚怎么样？"蒂米问。

"颜色不配。"布兰登
说，"我喜欢这枚。"

"大小不合适。"
凯莉说，"这一对好
看吗？差不多是最理
想的了！"

凯莉的眼光很准。这两枚纽扣缝在外婆的毛衣上可真漂亮。外婆高兴地说:"我觉得从今往后,我一定要把纽扣宝盒里面的扣子分门别类地放好。"

她真的做到了。

分 类

请你把这些纽扣按照不同的方式分类。

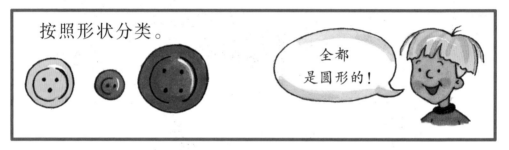

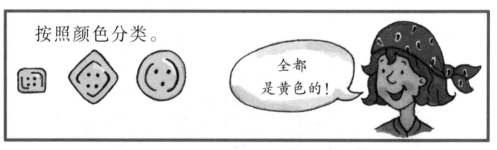

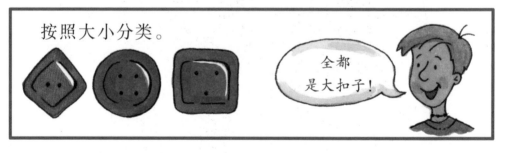

你还能想到其他的分类方法吗？

(提示：看看纽扣的扣眼有几个？)

亲爱的家长朋友,请您和孩子一起完成下面这些内容,会有更大的收获哟!

提高阅读能力

- 阅读封面,包括书名、作者等内容,然后和孩子聊聊,外婆的纽扣宝盒会是一个什么样的盒子? 这些纽扣是从哪里来的?她留着这些纽扣有什么用呢?她为什么要留这些纽扣呢?

- 读过故事后,看看能从封面图里找到多少枚纽扣?

- 凯莉不知道玩什么好,那么她怎么想到了外婆的纽扣宝盒? 答案可以在第 5 页找到。

- 凯莉和表兄弟想把纽扣按照形状来分类。他们找到了多少种形状? 请看第 16~17 页。

- 凯莉从外婆的纽扣宝盒得到了乐趣。为什么呢?请你至少说出一个理由。

- 外婆回家后凯莉他们吃了一惊,为什么呢?

巩固数学概念

- 请看第 32 页的内容。帮助孩子认识形状、大小和颜色。先请孩子按照形状来分类,然后再添加条件,比如,先找红色的纽扣,再找一个黄色的小纽扣,然后看看蓝色的方形大纽扣在哪里。

- 按照第 32 页的分类,请孩子找出所有黄色的大纽扣,或者所有两个扣眼的红色纽扣。也可以换一种方法来考考孩子,请孩子找出所有不是蓝色的纽扣。

- 请孩子在纸上画两组纽扣,再剪下来。一组大纽扣,一组小纽扣。让孩子用两种颜色的蜡笔给每组涂上不同的颜色。家长按照一定的规律来排列小纽扣,请孩子也按照同样的规律来排列大纽扣。

生活中的数学

- 为孩子找一袋纽扣,请孩子拿出一枚。在拿出之前,让孩子猜猜纽扣的形状和大小,扣眼有几个。

- 给孩子准备一个纽扣宝盒,请孩子用不同的方式给纽扣分类。

- 和孩子一起用纽扣玩游戏。准备一袋纽扣,每个参加游戏的人抓一把纽扣。每人留下七枚,剩下的放回去,并把自己的纽扣藏到身后。轮流问其他参加游戏的人有没有和自己相同的某种纽扣,比如,你可以问:"你有蓝色的纽扣吗?""你有四个扣眼的纽扣吗?"当其他参加游戏的人正好有同样的纽扣时,你们就可以把这对纽扣放在一起。第一个把手里的纽扣全部配对的人就是赢家了。

糖果盒

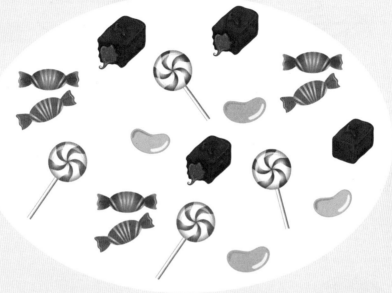

请你试着把桌子上的糖果分类放入下面
的糖果盒吧!

你最喜欢吃哪种糖果呢?

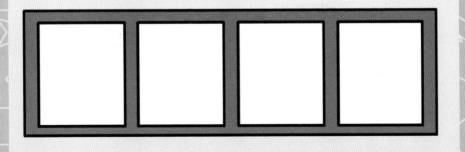

收衣服

这些衣服能分为哪几类？请你快来帮忙把衣服分类收好吧！

要洗到什么时候呢？

凯莉竟然要洗这么多的东西，看得她头都晕了呢！

快来帮她把餐具分类摆整齐吧！

我爱插花

请你把下面这些漂亮的花插进花瓶里吧！怎么分配才漂亮呢？

一共有三个花瓶，正好有三种花，所以一个花瓶放一种就行！你说呢？

你想怎么分？

我觉得按花的颜色来分，也是不错的选择哟！那每个花瓶里应该放几朵呢？

摆整齐

请你数一数我们一家三口每人有几双鞋。

请你按鞋的种类，将它们整齐地摆进鞋柜吧！

认一认 分一分

挑战一:快速说出每种图形的名称。

挑战二:快速按颜色进行分类。

挑战三:快速按形状进行分类。

参考答案

互动练习1：

巧克力　　棒棒糖　　水果糖　　橡皮糖

互动练习2：

短袖衫　　背心　　连衣裙　　裤子

互动练习3：

碟子　　碗　　杯子　　叉子　　勺子

互动练习4：
按颜色分：

互动练习5：
(1)按人分：

凯莉的鞋　　外婆的鞋　　蒂米的鞋

(2)按种类分：

冬季鞋　　单鞋　　凉鞋

互动练习6：
挑战一：略
挑战二：可分为红色与绿色
挑战三：可分为三角形、长方形、正方形、圆形、正方体、长方体、球、圆柱

互动练习7：
分法一：

文具　　书　　本子

分法二：

文具类　　语文类　　数学类　　英语类

（习题设计：骆　双、郝海霞）

42

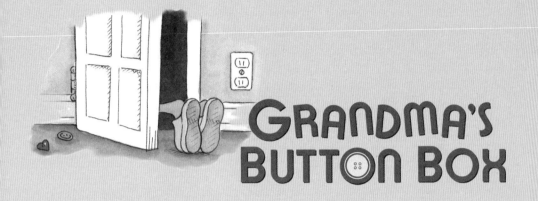

GRANDMA'S BUTTON BOX

Kelly and her cousins were visiting Grandma. One morning Kelly woke up to a very quiet house. Her three cousins were asleep. Grandma was taking a walk.

Kelly ate breakfast by herself and wondered what to do.

"What can I do that won't wake everyone up?" she thought. "Television's too loud. Piano's too loud. Even shooting baskets is too loud."

Then, while Kelly was getting dressed, she heard a tiny ping! A button had popped off her shirt.

"That's it!" she said. "Grandma's button box!"

Grandma had the coolest buttons! Even the plain ones seemed special, because Grandma told stories about them.

There were pearl buttons from Grandma's wedding dress and train buttons from Kelly's baby sweater. There was a soft furry button and a fancy gold one with big jewels on it.

Kelly hadn't played with the button box all summer. "It's the perfect quiet thing to do!" she thought.

The button box was on a high shelf next to Grandma's sewing table. Kelly had to stand on a stool to reach it.

She reached up as high as she could.

Grandma's button box wobbled. The top snapped open. Buttons flew everywhere. CRASH! The box hit the floor.

Timmy and Brendan came running down the hall.

"What happened?" asked Brendan. Then he saw the buttons. "Uh-oh," he said.

"You're in trouble now," said Timmy.

"You guys have to help me," said Kelly. "I'll never find all the buttons by myself."

"Sure," said Brendan.

"If you take me bowling," said Timmy.

"Deal," said Kelly.

Everyone started searching.

"Look! Here's one in the flowerpot," said Brendan.

"Here's one in Grandma's slipper!" shouted Timmy.

Kelly crawled into the closet. "There's a bunch of them in here!" she yelled.

"Wow!" said Timmy. "I found six under the rug."

Soon all the buttons were in a big pile.

"What a mess!" said Timmy. "I'll put them back in the box."

"Wait!" said Kelly. "We have to put them back in the right compartments."

"How did Grandma have them sorted?" asked Brendan. "By size? Shape? Color?"

"I can't remember," said Kelly.

"Uh-oh," said Brendan.

"You're in BIG trouble now!" said Timmy.

"Maybe they were sorted by shape," said Kelly.

"Let's try it," said Brendan.

Timmy picked out all the round buttons.

Brendan found some square ones and a few that were shaped like triangles and diamonds.

Kelly started to pick out everything else. She found star shapes, ducks, boats, and cowboy boots. There was an umbrella, two apples, an elephant, and a pineapple.

"How do I sort these?" she asked.

"You've got me," said Brendan.

"How about sorting them by size?" said Kelly.

"You mean we have to do it again?" said Timmy.

After a while, they had seven piles of buttons.

"Let's see," said Kelly. "We've got teeny, small, medium, large, extra-large, jumbo, and humongous."

Kelly sighed. "This isn't right, either."

"There are twelve compartments," said Brendan, "and only seven sizes."

"I GIVE UP!" yelled Timmy.

"What's all the shouting about?" asked Sara, Kelly's oldest cousin.

"Kelly spilled Grandma's buttons, and now they're all mixed up," Timmy said.

"We tried sorting them by shape," said Kelly.

"But that didn't work," said Timmy.

"We tried sorting them by size," said Brendan.

"And that didn't work either," said Timmy.

Sara looked at the buttons. "There must be another way," she said. "What about..."

"Sorting them by color!" said Kelly.

"Exactly," Sara said.

Sara and Kelly picked out the buttons that were white, pink, purple, yellow, orange, and brown.

Brendan and Timmy picked out the buttons that were red, blue, green, silver, gold, and black.

"We've got twelve colors," said Kelly.

"A color for every compartment!" Brendan said. "Perfect."

"Finally," said Timmy.

"Hi, kids!" called Grandma a few minutes later. "I'm home!"

"We're in the sewing room," called Sara.

"Oh, my goodness!" said Grandma. "You sorted my buttons!"

"Kelly spilled them," Timmy said. "But we found them all."

"We put them back by color," said Kelly. "That's the way you had them, isn't it?"

"No," said Grandma. "It isn't."

"You're in GIGANTIC trouble now," Timmy said to Kelly.

Grandma laughed. "I never sorted them, honey bunny," she told Kelly. "They were always just jumbled together."

"All that trouble for nothing?" said Timmy.

"It wasn't for nothing," said Grandma. She took off her sweater. "See these safety pins? I never bothered to look for new buttons because it always took so long to find anything in that button box."

"Let's look for some new buttons now," Kelly said. "It won't take long at all."

"How about this one?" asked Timmy.

"Wrong color," said Brendan. "I like this one."

"Wrong size," said Kelly. "How about these? They're almost perfect."

Kelly was right. The buttons looked great on Grandma's sweater. "I think I'll keep my buttons sorted from now on," she said.

And she did.